They stuck the pole in the ground, and Christopher Robin tied a message to it: NOI POLE DISCOVERED BY POOH — POOH FOUND IT.

Put the pole and the sign on this page.

Tiggers Don't Climb Trees

Tigger, a Very Bouncy Animal, told Roo (who wanted to know) all about the things that Tiggers could do.

"Can Tiggers climb trees?" Roo asked.

"Climbing trees is what they do best," said Tigger. "Better than Poohs. Of course, there's the coming-down too. . . ."
"Come on," squeaked Roo. "It's easy."

A. A. Milne

WINNIE-THE-POOH GOES EXPLORING

with illustrations after the style of
E. H. Shepard

Methuen Children's Books • London

Expotition To The North Pole

They all went off to discover the Pole,
Owl and Piglet and Rabbit and all.
Eeyore, Christopher Robin and Pooh . . .
And Rabbit's relations all went too.

"Pooh's found the North Pole," said Christopher Robin. "Isn't that lovely?"

Put Rabbit on this page.

"Ow," Tigger shouted. Then there was a crash, and a confused heap of Christopher Robin and Pooh and Piglet, and underneath everybody else was Eeyore.

Put Tigger and Roo and the broken branches on this page.

The Terrible Flood

Piglet wrote:
HELP! PIGLET (ME)

Then he put the paper in the bottle and threw the bottle as far as he could throw — *splash!*

Put the bottle and the floating honey pot on this page.

"Oh, Pooh Bear, what shall we do?" asked Christopher Robin.
"We might go in your umbrella," said Pooh.
Suddenly Christopher saw they might.

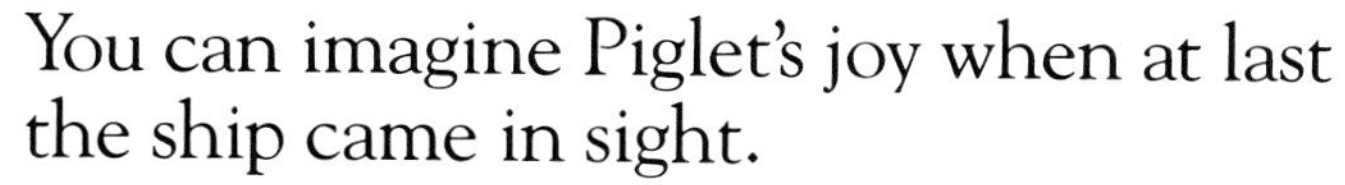

You can imagine Piglet's joy when at last the ship came in sight.

Put the boots on Christopher Robin.

Winnie-The-Pooh And Some Bees

"When you go after honey with a balloon," said Pooh, "the great thing is not to let the bees know you're coming."

"I shall try to look like a small black cloud. And you, Christopher Robin, walk up and down with your umbrella, saying, 'Tut-tut, it looks like rain.' "

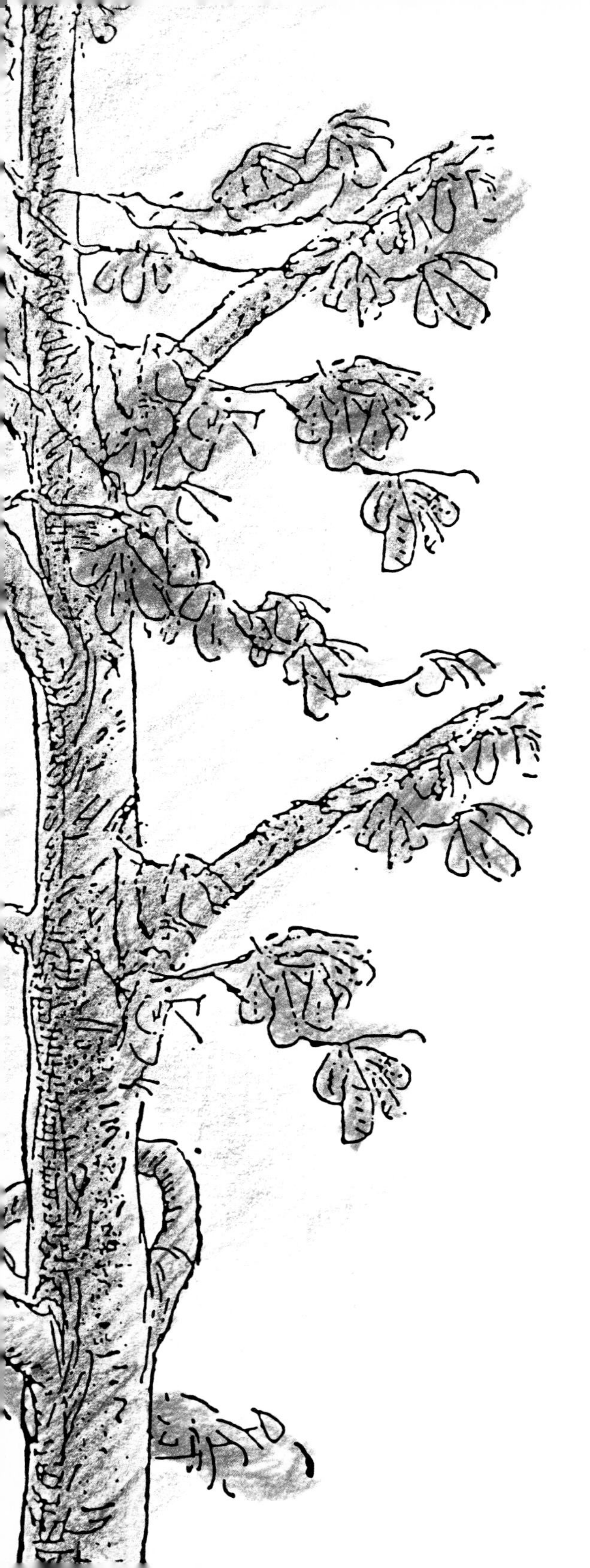

One bee sat down on the nose of the cloud for a moment, and then got up again.

"Christopher — OW! — Robin," called out the cloud, "I have come to a very important decision. *These are the wrong sort of bees.*"

Put Pooh and the bees on this page.

Pooh Gets Stuck

"Oh, help!" said Pooh. "I'd better go back."

"Oh, bother!" said Pooh. "I shall have to go on."

"I can't do either," said Pooh. "Oh help *and* bother!"

"The fact is," said Rabbit, "you're stuck. I shall go and fetch Christopher Robin."

"There's only one thing to be done," Christopher Robin said. "We shall have to wait for you to get thin again."

And at the end of the week Christopher Robin said, *"Now!"*

Put the dragonfly, butterfly and Rabbit's friends and relations on these pages.

Roo Falls In!

There came a sudden squeak from Roo, a splash, and a loud cry of alarm from Kanga.

"Look at me swimming!" squeaked Roo from the middle of the pool, as he was hurried down a waterfall into the next pool.

Two pools below, Pooh was standing with a long pole in his paws, and Kanga came up and took one end of it, and between them they held it across the lower part of the pool; and Roo, still bubbling proudly, "Look at me swimming," drifted up against it, and climbed out.

Put Roo and Owl on this page.

A Party For Pooh

"This party," said Christopher Robin, "is a party because of what someone did, and I've got a present for him."

"Here it is!" cried Christopher Robin excitedly. "Pass it down to silly old Pooh. It's for Pooh."

"For Pooh?" said Eeyore.

"Of course it is. The best bear in all the world."

"Thank-you," growled Pooh.

Put Pooh, Eeyore's tail and the present on these pages.

Pooh Bear's House

Put the compass and Six Pine Trees sign on this page.